GIOVANNI BATTISTA PERGOLESI

STABAT MATER

for Soprano, Alto, Strings and Basso continuo
für Sopran, Alt, Streicher und Basso continuo

Edited by/Herausgegeben von
Jürgen Neubacher

Ernst Eulenburg Ltd

London · Mainz · Madrid · New York · Paris · Prague · Tokyo · Toronto · Zürich

CONTENTS/INHALT

PREFACE / VORWORT

There is a tradition – not backed by documentary evidence – that Pergolesi composed his *Stabat mater* in response to a commission from a noble Neapolitan fraternity, the 'Cavalieri della Vergine dei Dolori', and that he completed the work while staying at Pozzuoli shortly before his death.[1] The work is said to have served as a replacement for the *Stabat mater* of the former *maestro di cappella* Alessandro Scarlatti (1660–1725), which had hitherto been performed annually on every Friday in March – a work with which it has certain features, albeit somewhat superficial ones, in common.[2] Another possible patron of the work, however, is Duke Marzio Domenico IV Carafa Maddaloni,[3] by whom Pergolesi is believed to have been employed between 1734 and his death on 16 March 1736.[4] It was doubtless also owing to the duke that Pergolesi was able to stay in Pozzuoli, a spa near Naples. He spent the last months of his life in the Franciscan monastery there, a foundation of the Carafa Maddaloni family,

Einer dokumentarisch ungesicherten Überlieferung zufolge soll Pergolesi sein *Stabat mater* im Auftrag einer adeligen neapolitanischen Bruderschaft, der „Cavalieri della Vergine dei Dolori", komponiert und kurz vor seinem Tod, während eines Aufenthalts in Pozzuoli, fertiggestellt haben[1]. Das Werk habe der Bruderschaft als Ersatz für das bis dahin jährlich an allen Freitagen des März aufgeführte *Stabat mater* des früheren Hofkapellmeisters Alessandro Scarlatti (1660 – 1725) dienen sollen, mit dem es einige, wenn auch eher äußerliche Gemeinsamkeiten aufzuweisen hat[2]. Als möglicher Auftraggeber wird jedoch auch Herzog Marzio Domenico IV Carafa Maddaloni gesehen[3], in dessen Diensten Pergolesi seit vermutlich 1734 bis zu seinem Tod am 16. März 1736 gestanden hat[4]. Dem Herzog verdankte Pergolesi wohl auch den Aufenthalt im nahe Neapel gelegenen Heilbad Pozzuoli, und zwar im dortigen Franziskanerkloster, einer Stiftung der Familie Carafa Maddaloni, wo er

---

[1] Marchese di Villarosa [i.e. Carlantonio de Rosa], *Lettera biografica intorno alla Patria ed alla Vita di Gio: Battista Pergolese celebre Compositore di Musica*, Naples, 1831; 2nd enlarged edn., Naples, 1843, pp. 25–27
[2] ibid.; for a comparative study of the two works, see Hermine H. Williams, 'The *Stabat Mater Dolorosa*: A Comparison of Settings by Alessandro Scarlatti and Giovanni Battista Pergolesi', in *Studi Pergolesiani/Pergolesi Studies 2*, ed. Francesco Degrada, Florence, 1988, pp. 144–154
[3] cf. Francesco Degrada, 'Lo "Stabat Mater" di Pergolesi e la parafrasi "Tilge, Höchster, meine Sünden" di Johann Sebastian Bach', in *Studi Pergolesiani*, pp. 155–184, esp. p. 180
[4] For new documents, see Francesco Degrada, 'Pergolesi, il marchese Pianetti e il Conservatorio di S. Maria di Loreto. Su alcune relazione tra Jesi e Napoli nel primo Settecento', in *Studi Pergolesiani 2*, pp. 20–48, esp. pp. 22f.

[1] Marchese di Villarosa [d. i. Carlantonio de Rosa], *Lettera biografica intorno alla Patria ed alla Vita di Gio: Battista Pergolese celebre Compositore di Musica* (Napoli 1831), 2., erweiterte Aufl., Napoli 1843, S. 25 – 27
[2] ibid.; eine vergleichende Untersuchung beider Werke unternahm Hermine H. Williams, *The 'Stabat Mater Dolorosa': a comparison of settings by Alessandro Scarlatti and Giovanni Battista Pergolesi*, in: *Studi Pergolesiani/Pergolesi Studies 2*, hg. von Francesco Degrada, Firenze 1988, S. 144 – 154.
[3] vgl. Francesco Degrada, *Lo 'Stabat Mater' di Pergolesi e la parafrasi 'Tilge Höchster meine Sünden' di Johann Sebastian Bach*, in: *Studi Pergolesiani 2*, S. 155 – 184, speziell S. 180
[4] neue Dokumente bei Francesco Degrada, *Pergolesi, il marchese Pianetti e il Conservatorio di Sancta Maria di Loreto. Su alcune relazioni tra Jesi e Napoli nel primo Settecento*, in: *Studi Pergolesiani 2*, S. 20 – 48, speziell S. 22f.

hoping to cure the tuberculosis that was to lead to his premature death.[5]

The work attracted notice very soon after Pergolesi's death and became widely known throughout Europe. Charles de Brosses, a traveller in Italy, reported as early as 1739 that the *Stabat mater* 'is regarded [...] as a masterpiece of Latin music. There is scarcely a piece more renowned for its profound harmonic skill.'[6] Among the many adaptations and arrangements of the work, a number deserve special mention: Johann Sebastian Bach's parody of 1746/47, using a free German rendering of the fifty-first Psalm ('Tilge, Höchster, meine Sünden');[7] *An Ode of Mr. Pope's* ['Vital sparks of heav'nly flame'] *Adapted to the Principal Airs of the Hymn Stabat Mater*, an arrangement printed in London in 1761; the edition produced by Johann Adam Hiller, using a German text by Friedrich Gottlieb Klopstock;[8] and Giovanni Paisiello's arrangement for orchestra and four-part male choir, published in Paris in 1810.[9]

während der letzten Monate seines Lebens eine schließlich zum frühzeitigen Tod führende Erkrankung an Tuberkulose[5] zu kurieren suchte.

Schon bald nach Pergolesis Tod fand das Werk Beachtung und Verbreitung in ganz Europa. So berichtete der Italienreisende Charles de Brosses bereits 1739, das *Stabat mater* werde „als ein Meisterwerk der lateinischen Musik angesehen", und es gebe „kaum ein Stück, das mehr als dieses hinsichtlich seiner tiefgehenden Kenntnis der Akkordverbindungen gelobt wird"[6]. Unter den zahlreichen Adaptionen und Bearbeitungen des Werkes verdienen Interesse eine um 1746/47 von Johann Sebastian Bach vorgenommene Parodie auf eine deutschsprachige Nachdichtung des 51. Psalms (*Tilge, Höchster, meine Sünden*)[7], die 1761 in London gedruckte Bearbeitung *An Ode of Mr. Pope's* [d. i. *Vital sparks of heav'nly flame*] *Adapted to the Principal Airs of the Hymn Stabat Mater*, die von Johann Adam Hiller erstellte Ausgabe auf eine deutsche Textfassung Friedrich Gottlieb Klopstocks[8] sowie Giovanni Paisiellos 1810 in Paris veröffentlichte Bearbeitung für Orchester und vierstimmigen Männerchor[9].

[5] ibid.
[6] 'On regarde [...] son *Stabat Mater*, comme le chef-d'œuvre de la musique latine. Il n'y a guère de pièce plus vantée que celle-ci pour la profonde science des accords' (Charles de Brosses, *Lettres familières sur l'Italie*, ed. Yvonne Bezard, Paris, 1931, vol. 2, p. 366)
[7] Johann Sebastian Bach, *Psalm 51 nach dem „Stabat mater" von Giovanni Battista Pergolesi (1710–1736) für Sopran, Alt, zwei Violinen und Basso continuo*, ed. Diethard Hellmann, Neuhausen-Stuttgart, 1990
[8] First published in a version for voices and keyboard (Leipzig, 1774), and later in a scored version, 'with improved harmony, strengthened with oboes and flutes and arranged for 4 vocal parts' (Leipzig, 1776)
[9] cf. Adelmo Damerini, *Lo „Stabat Mater" di Pergolesi in una rara trascrizione di Paisiello*, Florence, 1953

[5] ibid.
[6] „On regarde [...] son *Stabat Mater*, comme le chef-d'œuvre de la musique latine. Il n'y a guère de pièce plus vantée que celle-ci pour la profonde science des accords" (Charles de Brosses, *Lettres familières sur l'Italie*, hg. von Yvonne Bezard, Paris 1931, Bd. 2, S. 366).
[7] Johann Sebastian Bach, *Psalm 51 nach dem „Stabat mater" von Giovanni Battista Pergolesi (1710–1736) für Sopran, Alt, zwei Violinen, Viola und Basso continuo*, hg. von Diethard Hellmann, Neuhausen-Stuttgart 1990
[8] zunächst veröffentlicht in einer Fassung für Gesang und Klavier (Leipzig 1774), später als Partitur, und zwar „in der Harmonie verbessert, mit Oboen und Flöten verstärkt und auf 4 Singstimmen gebracht" (Leipzig 1776)
[9] vgl. Adelmo Damerini, *Lo „Stabat Mater" di Pergolesi in una rara trascrizione di Paisiello*, Firenze 1953

The composition's rapidly growing renown, and its continuing popularity, were matched by the appearance of a considerable number of printed editions (the first by J. Walsh, London, 1749) and countless manuscript copies. As far as the poor reliability of most of these copies is concerned, and as a pointer to the state of the sources generally, Hiller's prefatory note to his keyboard edition of 1774 is instructive: 'The score I have followed in writing this edition is a copy of another copy; for even the score engraved in copper in England is no more than a copy, and indeed a very imperfect one.'[10] Despite such drawbacks, however, the present new edition, while based on the autograph as its principal source, also takes account of some of these early copies, all of them dated to the middle of the eighteenth century or earlier by the libraries in which they are held (cf. Editorial Notes). That said, this edition adheres closely to the autograph – or rather to a photographic copy held in the Conservatorio di Musica S. Cecilia in Rome, since it has not been possible to obtain access to the original, which is in the library of the abbey of Montecassino.

The last page of the autograph contains a note of ownership from 1771, citing the Neapolitan *maestro di cappella* Giuseppe de Majo (1697–1771) as the previous owner and maintaining that de Majo claimed to have received it from Pergolesi as a memento before the latter's death: 'Questo è *Lo Stabat Mater*, Originale del Pergolesi, il quale mi fu regalato dal Sig[no]re D. Giuseppe de' Majo, Maestro della Cappella Reale, a dì 26. 7bre [settembre] 1771, il quale de' Majo mi disse che il sud [detto] Pergolesi gli feci questo dona-

Dem raschen und anhaltenden Ruhm der Komposition entsprach eine weitreichende Verbreitung durch mehrere Drucke (zuerst bei J. Walsh, London 1749) und unzählige Abschriften. Bezeichnend für die geringe Verläßlichkeit eines Großteils dieser Abschriften und für die Quellenlage insgesamt ist folgende Bemerkung Hillers im Vorbericht seines Klavierauszugs von 1774: „Die Partitur, nach welcher ich den Auszug geschrieben habe, ist eine Copie von einer andern Copie: denn selbst die in England in Kupfer gestochene Partitur ist nichts als Copie, und noch dazu eine sehr fehlerhafte"[10]. Trotz dieser Einschränkung wurde vom Herausgeber neben dem als Hauptquelle dienenden Autograph zu Vergleichszwecken auch Einblick in einige frühe Abschriften genommen, durchweg solche, die von den besitzenden Bibliotheken auf Mitte des 18. Jahrhunderts oder früher datiert werden (vgl. Revisionsbericht). Die Ausgabe folgt dennoch streng dem Autograph, wobei auf einen im Conservatorio di Musica S. Cecilia in Rom aufbewahrten Fotoabzug zurückgegriffen werden mußte, da das heute in der Bibliothek der Abtei Montecassino befindliche Original nicht zugänglich war.

Auf seiner letzten Seite trägt das Autograph einen Besitzvermerk aus dem Jahr 1771, der auf den neapolitanischen Hofkapellmeister Giuseppe de Majo (1697–1771) als Vorbesitzer verweist und besagt, daß dieser es von Pergolesi vor dessen Tod als Andenken geschenkt bekommen haben will: „Questo è *Lo Stabat Mater*, Originale del Pergolesi, il quale mi fu regalato dal Sig[no]re D. Giuseppe de' Majo, Maestro della Cappella Reale, a dì 26. 7bre[settembre] 1771, il quale de' Majo mi disse che il sud[detto] Pergolesi gli feci

---

[10] *Johann Baptist Pergolesi, Stabat Mater, oder Passions-Cantate, mit der deutschen Parodie des Herrn Klopstocks, in einem Clavierauszuge,* Leipzig, Bernhard Christoph Breitkopf & Sohn, 1774, 'Vorbericht'

[10] *Johann Baptist Pergolesi, Stabat Mater, oder Passions-Cantate, mit der deutschen Parodie des Herrn Klopstocks, in einem Clavierauszuge,* Leipzig: Bernhard Christoph Breitkopf & Sohn 1774, *Vorbericht*

tivo, per suo ricordo, prima della sua morte.'[11] Recently a link has been established between this note and the claim recorded by Marchese di Villarosa that Francesco Feo (1691–1761), the *maestro di musica* active in Naples, visited Pergolesi several times during the last months in Pozzuoli and found him at work on the *Stabat mater*.[12] It may, in fact, have been Feo who received the autograph as a gift from Pergolesi (though not, of course, before a copy had been prepared for the patron); de Majo, who was the husband of a niece of Feo's, may then have inherited it from his relative, who had no direct heirs.[13]

As the photographic copy clearly indicates, the autograph consists of twelve fascicles, or sections, containing varying numbers of sheets (cf. Editorial Notes). It is notable that in writing out some of the movements Pergolesi started a new section of paper, despite that fact that pages with uninscribed staves were available on the sheets of the preceding section. This applies, especially, to Nos. 6 and 10 (in each case, two uninscribed pages at the end of the preceding section) and to No. 12 (three uninscribed preceding pages). This extravagant use of paper, for which there must have been some external reason, gives scope for speculation about the genesis of the composition. It is possible that Pergolesi began the composition at different points in the work, and that the empty

[11] 'This is the *Stabat Mater*, the original of Pergolesi, which was presented to me by Giuseppe de Majo, Master of the Royal Chapel, on 26 September 1771 and which de Majo told me the aforementioned Pergolesi had given to him, as a memento, before his death.'

[12] cf. note 1 above

[13] cf. Hanns-Bertold Dietz, 'Durante, Feo and Pergolesi: Concerning Misattributions among their Sacred Music', in *Studi Pergolesiani 2*, pp. 128–143, esp. p. 134

questo donativo, per suo ricordo, prima della sua morte"[11]. Neuerdings wird eine Verbindung hergestellt zwischen dieser Notiz und dem durch den Marchese di Villarosa überlieferten Hinweis, daß der in Neapel tätige „Maestro di Musica" Francesco Feo (1691–1761) Pergolesi während der letzten Wochen in Pozzuoli mehrfach besucht und bei der Arbeit am *Stabat mater* angetroffen habe[12]: Es könnte demnach Feo gewesen sein, der das Autograph von Pergolesi geschenkt bekam (jedoch sicherlich erst, nachdem eine Abschrift für den Auftraggeber hergestellt worden war), und De Majo, Ehegatte einer Nichte Feos, könnte es von seinem ohne direkte Nachkommen verbliebenen Anverwandten geerbt haben[13].

Wie in der benutzten fotografischen Vorlage gut zu erkennen, setzt sich das Autograph aus zwölf Faszikeln (Lagen) mit unterschiedlicher Bogenzahl zusammen (vgl. Revisionsbericht). Es fällt auf, daß Pergolesi bei der Niederschrift einiger Sätze zu einer neuen Papierlage griff, obwohl auf den Bogen der vorhergehenden noch unbeschriebene rastrierte Seiten zur Verfügung standen. Dies gilt vor allem für Nr. 6 und Nr. 10 (in beiden Fällen am Ende der vorhergehenden Lage zwei unbeschriebene Seiten) sowie für Nr. 12 (drei unbeschriebene Seiten vorab). Dieser wohl einer äußeren Notwendigkeit entsprungene verschwenderische Umgang mit Papier gibt Anlaß zu Mutmaßungen über die Entstehung der Komposition: Entweder begann Pergolesi die Komposition

[11] „Dies ist das *Stabat Mater*, Pergolesis Original, welches mir Giuseppe de Majo, Kapellmeister der Königlichen Kapelle, am 26. September 1771 schenkte und welches ihm, wie mir De Majo sagte, der oben erwähnte Pergolesi vor seinem Tod als Andenken zum Geschenk gemacht hatte."

[12] wie Anm. 1

[13] vgl. Hanns-Bertold Dietz, *Durante, Feo, and Pergolesi: concerning misattributions among their sacred music*, in: *Studi Pergolesiani 2*, S. 128–143, speziell S. 134

pages at the ends of certain movements arose because an ensuing movement or group of movements had already been begun, or completed, on another fascicle. The presence of empty pages could also indicate that there was a gap in time between different spells of work on specific parts of the composition. Alternatively, it is possible that Pergolesi, severely pressed for time, immediately sent off for copying those parts of the work that he had already completed and that he therefore had to avail himself of a new section of paper when writing out the ensuing part of the work, despite the fact that empty pages remained on the sheets that had been handed over. This possibility would be consistent with the story reported by Marchese di Villarosa that Pergolesi, despite Francesco Feo's exhortations to think of his state of health, refused to interrupt his work on the *Stabat mater*, on the grounds that he was obliged to his patron for an advance payment of ten ducats and, since he felt very weak and exhausted, did not know whether he would actually be able to complete his task.[14] To clear these questions up completely we should need to examine the state of the paper and the ink used in the individual fascicles; the editor, however, has been unable to do this owing to lack of access to the autograph.

The autograph is clearly a compositional draft, inasmuch as it contains corrections, deletions and a hasty or inconsistent use of accidentals and expression marks. Dynamics and articulation occasionally need to be supplied by the performers.

In conformity with a tradition particularly common in Italy and France during the seventeenth and eighteenth centuries,

an unterschiedlichen Stellen, so daß sich die leeren Seiten am Ende einiger Sätze damit erklären ließen, daß ein sich anschließender Satz oder Satzkomplex bereits begonnen oder fertiggestellt auf einem anderen Faszikel vorlag. Dies könnte zugleich ein Indiz sein für ein zeitliches Auseinanderliegen der Arbeit an einzelnen Werkteilen. Denkbar wäre aber auch, daß Pergolesi, unter großem Zeitdruck stehend, bereits fertiggestellte Teile gleich zur Abschrift weitergab und somit, ungeachtet noch leerer Seiten auf den weggegebenen Bogen, für die Niederschrift des sich anschließenden Teils zu einer neuen Papierlage greifen mußte. Diese Möglichkeit stünde in Übereinstimmung mit der durch den Marchese di Villarosa überlieferten Darstellung, Pergolesi habe trotz der Mahnungen Francesco Feos, Rücksicht auf seinen Gesundheitszustand zu nehmen, die Arbeit am *Stabat mater* nicht unterbrechen wollen, mit der Begründung, er sei durch eine Vorauszahlung von 10 Dukaten dem Auftraggeber verpflichtet und wisse nicht, da er sich sehr schwach und erschöpft fühle, ob er mit der Arbeit überhaupt zu Ende komme[14]. Eine vollständige Klärung des angedeuteten Sachverhalts setzt jedoch eine Untersuchung auch der Papierbeschaffenheit und der verwendeten Tinte der einzelnen Faszikel voraus, was aber dem Herausgeber wegen der Unzugänglichkeit des Autographs nicht möglich war.

Das Autograph trägt deutliche Züge einer Kompositionsniederschrift mit typischen Merkmalen wie Korrekturen, Ausstreichungen und Flüchtigkeiten bzw. Inkonsequenzen bei der Setzung von Akzidentien und Vortragszeichen. Dynamik und Artikulation bedürfen gelegentlich der Ergänzung durch die Ausführenden.

Einer insbesondere in Italien und Frankreich im 17. und 18. Jahrhundert verbreiteten Tradition folgend gebraucht

---

[14] cf. note 1 above

[14] wie Anm. 1

Pergolesi uses the term *dolce* instead of *piano*, possibly to indicate an emotional effect as well as a dynamic level.[15] In addition to *dolce* and *forte*, his dynamic gradations include the reductions *dolce assai*, *più dolce* (both roughly equivalent to *pianissimo*) and *sotto voce* and the increase *forte assai* (i.e. *fortissimo*). The use of *dolce* at the beginning of a phrase and *forte* at the end of the phrase indicates a crescendo (see, for example, No. 5, bars 32–38), while the use of *forte* and *dolce* in immediate succession probably indicates a sforzato (see, for example, No. 2, bars 59–60 and No. 9, bar 6). The instruction *lasciare* at the beginning of No. 12 applies to the players in the basso continuo group and indicates – together with the use of quaver rests – that the sound should be 'left' or released: the notes, in other words, should not be held too long, but played shorter than written.[16]

[15] In the article 'Doux' in his *Dictionnaire de musique* (Paris, 1768, p. 178) Jean-Jacques Rousseau writes: 'Ce mot en Musique est opposé à *Fort* [...] Les Italiens écrivent *dolce* & plus communément *piano* dans le même sens; mais leurs Puristes en Musique soutiennent que ces deux mots ne sont pas synonymes, & que c'est par abus que plusieurs Auteurs les emploient comme tels. Ils disent que *piano* signifie simplement une modération de Son, une diminution de bruit; mais que *dolce* indique, outre cela, une manière de jouer *più soave*, plus douce, plus liée, & répondant à-peu-près au mot *Louré* des François.' ('In music this word is the opposite of *Fort* [...] The Italians write *dolce* and, more commonly, *piano* in the same sense; but their musical purists maintain that these two words are not synonyms and, that it is a misuse on the part of several authors when they are treated as such. They say that *piano* signifies simply a moderation of the sound, a lessening of volume; but that *dolce* indicates, in addition, a manner of playing that is *più soave*, more gentle, more smoothy joined, corresponding somewhat to the French word *Louré*.')

[16] Francesco Degrada kindly points out that this performing instruction is commonly used by Pergolesi and his contemporaries.

Pergolesi anstelle von *piano* die Bezeichnung *dolce*, worin ein Affektcharakter mitschwingen könnte[15]. Neben *dolce* und *forte* umfaßt die Skala der dynamischen Abstufungen *dolce assai*, *più dolce* (beide etwa gleichbedeutend mit *pianissimo*) und *sotto voce* als Abschwächungen sowie *forte assai* (d. h. *fortissimo*) als Verstärkung. *Dolce* zu Beginn und *forte* am Ende einer Phrase deuten auf ein Crescendo hin (z. B. Nr. 5, T. 32 – 38), und die unmittelbare Aufeinanderfolge von *forte* und *dolce* meint wohl ein Sforzato (z. B. Nr. 2, T. 59/60; Nr. 9, T. 6).

Die Vorschrift *lasciare* zu Beginn von Nr. 12 richtet sich an die Spieler der Bassocontinuo-Gruppe und fordert ein – hier zusätzlich durch Achtelpausen angezeigtes – Verlassen des Tones, ist also eine Anweisung, die Noten nicht zu lang, das heißt eher kürzer als notiert zu spielen[16].

[15] Im Artikel *Doux* seines *Dictionnaire de Musique* (Paris 1768, S. 178) schreibt Jean-Jacques Rousseau: „Ce mot en Musique est opposé à *Fort* [...] Les Italiens écrivent *dolce* & plus communément *piano* dans le même sens; mais leurs Puristes en Musique soutiennent que ces deux mots ne sont pas synonymes, & que c'est par abus que plusieurs Auteurs les emploient comme tels. Ils disent que *piano* signifie simplement une modération de Son, une diminution de bruit; mais que *dolce* indique, outre cela, une manière de jouer *più soave*, plus douce, plus liée, & répondant à-peu-près au mot *Louré* des François." („Dieses Wort bedeutet in der Musik das Gegenteil von *Forte* [...] Die Italiener schreiben *dolce* und, gewöhnlicher, *piano* im gleichen Sinn; aber ihre Musikpuristen behaupten, daß diese beiden Wörter keine Synonyme sind und viele Autoren diese mißbräuchlich als solche verwenden. Sie sagen, daß *piano* lediglich eine Klangabschwächung, eine Verminderung der Lautstärke bedeute; während *dolce* darüber hinaus anzeigt, daß man *più soave* spielen soll, weicher, gebundener, was in etwa dem französischen Wort *louré* [gebunden] entsprechen dürfte.")

[16] Laut freundlichem Hinweis von Francesco Degrada handelt es sich hierbei um eine bei Pergolesi und Zeitgenossen durchaus gewöhnliche Spielanweisung.

The only ornament sign Pergolesi uses, apart from appoggiaturas, is a curved or wavy line followed by a point (⌢ or ⌣). Although a trill may not be intended in every such case – other forms of ornamentation such as a vibrato may sometimes be meant – this sign has consistently been reproduced as *tr* in the present edition.

The markings 'Siegue Canto solo' or 'Siegue Alto solo' placed at the end of a movement to draw attention to what follows, do not indicate a contrast between choric and solistic writing but are a device, commonly used at the time, for drawing attention to the exposed role of a particular part as it stands out amid the overall body of voices. The style and texture of the composition undoubtedly call for a consistently solistic method of vocal performance. The instrumentation of the basso continuo part is not given precise specification in the autograph, but the part divisions in No. 8 (bars 9ff. and 19ff.) and No. 12 (bars 36ff. and 48ff; cf. *Einzelanmerkungen*) imply a 'Violoncello' and an additional bass instrument (double bass or violone), and also at least one, or more than one, chordal instrument to realize the figured bass (e.g. organ or lute). There is considerable evidence[17] that an archlute was used as a continuo instrument in the Neapolitan church music of the eighteenth century, and Pergolesi himself called for one in the fragmentary autograph arrangement of his Mass in F major for five-part choir and double orchestra (Naples, Conservatorio di Musica S. Pietro a Majella, Rari 1.6.27): 'P[rim]o coro: Org[ano] e Contrabasso; [Secondo coro:] Viol[oncel]lo e Leuto e Contrabasso'.[18]

Das von Pergolesi ausschließlich verwendete Verzierungszeichen, sieht man von Vorschlagsnoten ab, besteht aus einer gekrümmten oder welligen Linie mit nachfolgendem Punkt (⌢ oder ⌣). Obwohl nicht in allen Fällen ein Triller gemeint sein dürfte, sondern auch an andere Verzierungsformen wie beispielsweise ein Vibrato zu denken ist, wurde das Zeichen in der vorliegenden Ausgabe einheitlich durch *tr* wiedergegeben.

Der an den Satzenden gelegentlich auftretende Folgevermerk „Siegue Canto solo" oder „Siegue Alto solo" bezieht sich keineswegs auf einen Gegensatz von chorischer und solistischer Besetzung der Vokalstimmen, sondern ist ein zeitüblicher Hinweis auf die exponierte Funktiôn einer aus dem Stimmenverband heraustretenden Einzelstimme. Stil und Faktur der Komposition verlangen ohne Zweifel eine durchgehend solistische Ausführung der Vokalstimmen. Die Besetzung der im Autograph nicht näher bezeichneten Basso-continuo-Stimme erfordert neben dem aus Stimmaufspaltungen in Nr. 8 (T. 9ff. und 19ff.) und Nr. 12 (T. 36ff. und 48ff.; vgl. *Einzelanmerkungen*) zu erschließenden „Violoncello" sowie einem weiteren Baßinstrument (Kontrabaß oder Violone) mindestens ein, wenn nicht mehrere Akkordinstrumente zur Ausführung der Bezifferung (z. B. Orgel oder Laute). Die Mitwirkung einer Erzlaute unter den Continuo-Instrumenten ist für die neapolitanische Kirchenmusik des 18. Jahrhunderts mehrfach bezeugt[17] und wird auch von Pergolesi selbst in der Torso gebliebenen autographen Bearbeitung seiner Messe F-Dur für fünfstimmigen Chor und doppeltes Orchester (Napoli, Conservatorio di Musica S. Pietro a Majella, Rari 1.6.27) verlangt: „P[rim]o coro: Org[ano] e

---

[17] cf. Helmut Hucke, 'Pergolesi's *Missa S. Emidio*', in *Music in the Classic Period: Essays in Honor of Barry S. Brook*, ed. Allan W. Atlas, New York, 1985, pp. 99–115, esp. pp. 106f.

[17] vgl. Helmut Hucke, *Pergolesi's 'Missa S. Emidio'*, in: *Music in the Classic Period. Essays in Honor of Barry S. Brook*, hg. von Allan W. Atlas, New York 1985, S. 99 – 115, spez. S. 106f.

A rhythmic alteration added in the closing bars of the autograph (in a sense, a composed ritardando; cf. *Einzelanmerkungen*) recurs in some early copies but not in others. It may have been made by Pergolesi himself but may, equally, be in another hand. If the alteration in the autograph is by Pergolesi himself, it would indicate – since copies with the unaltered version exist – that Pergolesi undertook the change at a stage when a copy of the original had already been made and that, for reasons unknown, the alteration was not subsequently made to the copy. This notional copy (possibly made for the work's patron) would then have been the basis for later copies which also retain the original version of the passage. Alternatively, if the alteration in the autograph is by another hand, there are two possible explanations: (a) the alteration may still be attributable to Pergolesi; he may, however, have made the change, not in his own score, but in a copy submitted to him for checking and then have neglected to enter the change in the original, either through oversight or because he had already parted with the original; the change would then have been added by another hand later. Copies containing the first (unaltered) version would, on this assumption, derive directly or indirectly from the uncorrected original. (b) The alteration may be an unauthorized change made by another person. The change may either have been made directly on to the autograph and have become current from there, or it may have been made when a later copy was being prepared and, likewise, have been given wider currency from that copy; the alteration would then, again, have been added to the autograph by

Contrabasso; [Secondo coro:] Viol[oncel]lo e Leuto e Contrabasso"[18].

Eine in den Schlußtakten des Autographs nachträglich vorgenommene rhythmische Veränderung (quasi ein auskomponiertes Ritardando; vgl. *Einzelanmerkungen*), die sich in einigen frühen Abschriften wiederfindet, in anderen dagegen nicht, könnte von Pergolesi selbst herrühren, aber auch von fremder Hand eingetragen worden sein. Im ersten Fall, wonach die Änderung im Autograph von Pergolesi selbst vorgenommen worden wäre, würde dies bedeuten, da Abschriften mit der ursprünglichen Lesart vorliegen, daß Pergolesi die Einzeichnung zu einem Zeitpunkt vorgenommen hätte, als bereits eine Abschrift von dem Original angefertigt worden war, und daß in dieser die Änderung aus unbekannten Gründen nicht mehr nachgetragen wurde. Auf diese hypothetische Abschrift (möglicherweise für den Auftraggeber des Werkes bestimmt) würden dann andere Abschriften, die ebenfalls die ursprüngliche Lesart aufweisen, zurückgehen. Im zweiten Fall, wonach die Änderung im Autograph von fremder Hand stammen würde, bestehen zwei Möglichkeiten: a) Die Änderung könnte dennoch auf Pergolesi zurückzuführen sein, falls er sie nämlich nicht in der eigenen Partitur, sondern in einer ihm zur Durchsicht vorgelegten Abschrift vorgenommen hätte und im Original, zum Beispiel aus Nachlässigkeit oder weil er dieses schon aus der Hand gegeben hatte, nicht mehr nachgetragen hat (dort wäre sie dann später von fremder Hand eingetragen worden). Abschriften, die die ursprüngliche Lesart aufweisen, würden dann direkt oder indirekt auf das unkorrigierte Original zurückgehen. b) Bei der Änderung könnte es sich um einen eigenmächtigen Eingriff

---

[18] Facsimile in *Opera omnia di Giov. Batt. Pergolesi*, ed. Filippo Caffarelli, vol. 6, Rome, 1940, p. [V]

[18] Faksimile in: *Opera omnia di Giov. Batt. Pergolesi*, hg. von Filippo Caffarelli, Bd. 6, Roma 1940, S. [V]

another hand later. Without an examination of the autograph itself, however, and a study of further sources, it is impossible to reach a firm conclusion about the authenticity of this rhythmic alteration to the 'Amen' ending.

A certain dissatisfaction with the shaping of the ending of the work is also suggested by the repeat of the concluding 'Amen' fugue that is indicated in several mutually independent sources – a performance tradition which has no basis in the autograph. A handwritten copy believed to date from the middle of the eighteenth century (Bergamo, Civico Istituto musicale Gaetano Donizetti, XXXV 8979 L) contains, at the end of the score, the marking 'Da Capo l'amen'. In a rejoinder to an anonymous newspaper article on a performance of the *Stabat mater*, the future Stockholm *Hovkapellmästare* Joseph Martin Kraus wrote in the *Stockholms Posten* on 10 May 1780: 'The gentleman's opinion on the last fugue ['Amen' fugue] appears equally remarkable, since the entire orchestra can testify that this piece must always be played twice on account of its brevity.'[19] Finally, Johann Sebastian Bach provides a full repeat of the 'Amen' fugue in the vocal and instrumental parts of

einer fremden Person handeln, der entweder im Autograph direkt vorgenommen wurde und von dort aus weitertradiert worden ist, oder aber der bei der Anfertigung einer späteren Abschrift erfolgte und von dieser aus Verbreitung fand. (Auch im letzten Fall wäre die Änderung dann später von unbekannter Hand im Autograph nachgetragen worden.) Eine Entscheidung über die Authentizität dieser rhythmischen Veränderung des „Amen"-Schlusses ist jedoch ohne Untersuchung am Autograph selbst und ohne das Studium weiterer Quellen nicht möglich.

Auf eine gewisse Unzufriedenheit mit der Schlußgestaltung des Werkes deutet auch eine in mehreren voneinander unabhängigen Quellen angezeigte Wiederholung der abschließenden „Amen"-Fuge hin, eine Aufführungtradition, für die das Autograph jedoch keine Anhaltspunkte bietet. In einer mutmaßlich um die Mitte des 18. Jahrhunderts angefertigten Handschrift (Bergamo, Civico Istituto musicale Gaetano Donizetti, XXXV 8979 L) findet sich am Schluß der Partitur der Vermerk „Da Capo l'amen". In einer Entgegnung auf einen anonymen Zeitungsartikel zu einer Aufführung des *Stabat mater* schrieb der spätere Stockholmer Hofkapellmeister Joseph Martin Kraus am 10. Mai 1780 in der *Stockholms Posten* (Übersetzung): „Was der Herr über die letzte Fuge [„Amen"-Fuge] äußert, scheint ebenso merkwürdig zu sein, da die ganze Kapelle bezeugen kann, daß dieses Stück aufgrund seiner Kürze immer zweimal gespielt werden muß"[19]. Johann Sebastian Bach schließlich ließ in

[19] 'Joseph Martin Kraus. Anonyme musikästhetische Beiträge der Stockholmer Zeit 1779-1781', translated with a commentary by Irmgard Leux-Henschen, in *Joseph Martin Kraus in seiner Zeit. Referate des zweiten internationalen Kraus-Symposiums in Buchen 1980*, ed. Friedrich W. Riedel (*Studien zur Landes- und Sozialgeschichte der Musik*, 5), Munich/Salzburg, 1982, pp. 181-217, esp. p. 209

[19] *Joseph Martin Kraus. Anonyme musikästhetische Beiträge der Stockholmer Zeit 1779-1781*, übersetzt u. kommentiert v. Irmgard Leux-Henschen, in: *Joseph Martin Kraus in seiner Zeit. Referate des zweiten internationalen Kraus-Symposiums in Buchen 1980*, hg. v. Friedrich W. Riedel (*Studien zur Landes- und Sozialgeschichte der Musik 5*), München-Salzburg 1982, S. 181-217, spez. S. 209

his Pergolesi arrangement; indeed, for the repeat, the accidentals are changed from minor to major.[20]

As far as the text of the hymn *Stabat mater* is concerned (countless variants of which have been preserved),[21] the present edition follows Pergolesi's autograph. As an Italian, Pergolesi would naturally have had in mind the Italian pronunciation of the Latin text, as is clear from several cases where consecutive vowels are elided into a single syllable in the Italian manner (cf. No. 10, bars 10, 22 and 25; No. 11, bars 19 and 26).

The editor wishes to thank the following libraries for granting permission to consult source materials held by them and for preparing microfilm copies: the Sächsische Landesbibliothek, Dresden; the Musikbibliothek der Stadt Leipzig; the Biblioteca nazionale, Naples; and the Conservatorio di Musica S. Cecilia, Rome. I am especially grateful to Dr Friedrich Lippmann of the Deutsches Historisches Institut in Rome for supplying photocopies and microfilm copies of sources B 1-3.

den Vokal- und Instrumentalstimmen seiner Pergolesi-Bearbeitung die „Amen"-Fuge vollständig wiederholen, und zwar beim zweiten Durchlauf durch Veränderung der Akzidentien in Dur statt Moll[20].

Hinsichtlich der Textfassung des in unzähligen Varianten überlieferten altkirchlichen Hymnus *Stabat mater*[21] folgt die vorliegende Ausgabe dem Autograph Pergolesis. Daß Pergolesi als Italiener selbstverständlich mit einer italienischen Aussprache des lateinischen Textes rechnete, geht aus mehreren für die italienische Sprache charakteristischen Verschleifungen aufeinanderfolgender Vokale zu einer einzigen Silbe hervor (vgl. Nr. 10, T. 10, 22 u. 25; Nr. 11, T. 19 u. 26).

Der Herausgeber dankt folgenden Bibliotheken für die Erlaubnis, von ihnen verwahrtes Quellenmaterial einzusehen, und für die Anfertigung von Mikrofilmkopien: Dresden, Sächsische Landesbibliothek; Leipzig, Musikbibliothek der Stadt Leipzig; Napoli, Biblioteca nazionale; Roma, Conservatorio di Musica S. Cecilia. Besonderer Dank gebührt Dr. Friedrich Lippmann vom Deutschen Historischen Institut Rom für die Beschaffung und Bereitstellung von Foto- und Mikrofilmkopien der Quellen B 1 - 3.

Editorial Notes

The sources

A Autograph score, head title: *Stabat Mater a 2 voci & V: V: - Pergolesi* (Montecassino, Abbazia); 37 oblong folios with twelve staves on each page (folios 12[r,v], 17[v], 21[v], 27[r,v], 32[v]-33[v] not inscribed),

Revisionsbericht

Die Quellen

A Autographe Partitur, Kopftitel: *Stabat Mater a 2 voci & V: V: - Pergolesi* (Montecassino, Abbazia); 37 Bll. im Querformat, beidseitig mit zwölf Systemen rastriert (Bl. 12[r,v], 17[v], 21[v], 27[r,v], 32[v]-33[v]

---

[20] cf. the new edition cited in note 7 above, and also Alfred Dürr, 'Neues über Bachs Pergolesi-Bearbeitung', in *Bach-Jahrbuch*, 54, 1968, pp. 89-100, esp. p. 96

[21] cf. the list of textual variants in *Analecta Hymnica Medii Aevi*, ed. Clemens Blume, vol. 54, Leipzig, 1915, pp. 312-318

[20] vgl. die in Anm. 7 genannte Neuausgabe sowie Alfred Dürr, *Neues über Bachs Pergolesi-Bearbeitung*, in: *Bach-Jahrbuch* 54, 1968, S. 89 - 100, speziell S. 96

[21] vgl. die Auflistung der Textvarianten in: *Analecta Hymnica Medii Aevi*, hg. von Clemens Blume, Bd. 54, Leipzig 1915, S. 312 - 318

arranged in 12 fascicles with varying numbers of sheets, mostly numbered (in another hand?) in the upper left-hand corner ([fascicle 1]: folios 1r–3v; [2]: 4r–6v; 3: 7r–10v; 4: 11r–12v; 5: 13r–14v; 6: 15r– 17v; 7: 18r–21v; 8: 22r–25v; 9: 26r–27v; 10: 28r–31v; 11: 32r–33v; 12: 34r–37v).

A photographic reproduction dating from the first half of the twentieth century is held in the Conservatorio di Musica S. Cecilia, Rome; a facsimile, excluding the pages not inscribed, is contained in volume 26 of the *Opera omnia di Giov. Batt. Pergolesi*, ed. Filippo Caffarelli, Rome, 1942, pp. I-XXXIII.

B Copies of the score by unknown copyists:

1 Bergamo, Civico Istituto musicale Gaetano Donizetti, XXXV 8979 L (mid-eighteenth century)
2 Bologna, Archivo del Convento di S. Francesco, M. P IV-4 (mid-eighteenth century)
3 ibid., FN. P. I. 3 (mid-eighteenth century)
4 Dresden, Sächsische Landesbibliothek, Mus. 3005-D-1b (c. 1750; formerly Katholische Hofkirche)
5 Leipzig, Musikbibliothek der Stadt Leipzig, PM 4130 (mid-eighteenth century?; formerly Musikbibliothek Peters, Leipzig)
6 Naples, Biblioteca nazionale Vittorio Emanuele III, MS S. Mart. 768 (first half of the eighteenth century; later owner's mark on the front flyleaf: 'Del Marchese di Cermignano')

Editorial principles

The present edition is a reproduction of source A. Deviations and variant readings in the B sources are recorded only if they

---

unbeschrieben), angeordnet in 12 Faszikeln mit unterschiedlicher Bogenzahl, diese zum überwiegenden Teil in der linken oberen Ecke (von fremder Hand?) numeriert ([Faszikel 1]: Bl. 1r– 3v; [2]: 4r–6v; 3: 7r–10v; 4: 11r–12v; 5: 13r–14v; 6: 15r–17v; 7: 18r–21v; 8: 22r–25v; 9: 26r–27v; 10: 28r–31v; 11: 32r–33v; 12: 34r–37v).

Eine fotografische Reproduktion aus der ersten Hälfte des 20. Jahrhunderts befindet sich im Conservatorio di Musica S. Cecilia, Rom; ein Faksimile, unter Auslassung der unbeschriebenen Seiten, ist enthalten in Band 26 der *Opera omnia di Giov. Batt. Pergolesi*, hg. v. Filippo Caffarelli, Roma 1942, S. I-XXXIII.

B Partiturabschriften unbekannter Schreiber:

1 Bergamo, Civico Istituto musicale Gaetano Donizetti, XXXV 8979 L (Mitte 18. Jahrhundert)
2 Bologna, Archivo del Convento di S. Francesco, M. P IV-4 (Mitte 18. Jahrhundert)
3 ibid., FN. P. I.3 (Mitte 18. Jahrhundert)
4 Dresden, Sächsische Landesbibliothek, Mus. 3005-D-1b (um 1750; vormals Katholische Hofkirche)
5 Leipzig, Musikbibliothek der Stadt Leipzig, PM 4130 (Mitte 18. Jahrhundert?; vormals Musikbibliothek Peters, Leipzig)
6 Napoli, Biblioteca nazionale Vittorio Emanuele III, MS S. Mart. 768 (1. Hälfte 18. Jahrhundert; späterer Besitzvermerk auf dem vorderen Vorsatzblatt: „Del Marchese di Cermignano")

Editionsprinzipien

Die vorliegende Ausgabe gibt die Lesart der Quelle A wieder. Abweichungen und Varianten der Quellengruppe B werden

shed light on points in A that are not clear or that are relevant to the history of transmission of the work. All editorial additions are enclosed within square brackets; editorial ties and slurs are shown with broken lines. Bars or staves which are not written out in A but which Pergolesi indicates by the abbreviations *unisono* and *col basso* have been silently added. Key signatures and the use of note-beams (the latter occasionally simplified) follow A, while the use of accidentals and the placing of note-stems has been adapted to modern notational practice.

Jürgen Neubacher
Translation Richard Deveson

nur mitgeteilt, sofern sie Unklarheiten in A zu erhellen vermögen oder überlieferungsgeschichtliche Bedeutung haben. Alle Herausgeberzusätze sind kenntlich gemacht durch eckige Klammern oder gestrichelte Bögen. Nicht ausgeschriebene Takte oder Systeme in A, in denen sich Pergolesi einer abkürzenden Notierung durch *unisono*- und *col basso*-Verweise bediente, wurden stillschweigend ausgefüllt. Tonartvorzeichnung und Balkensetzung (letztere gelegentlich vereinheitlicht) folgen A, während Akzidentiensetzung und Stielung den heute üblichen Stichregeln angepaßt wurden.

Jürgen Neubacher

Einzelanmerkungen

1. *Stabat mater dolorosa*

    A   Bl. 1^r–3^r (1. Akkol.)

Takt 5 A   Vl. II 3. N. mit *staccato*-Zeichen

    5–7 B$_{1-3,6}$ Vla.

    15 A   3.–4. N. mit Bogen

    47 A   „Siegue"

2. *Cuius animam gementem*

    A   Bl. 3^r (2. Akkol.) – 5^v (1. Akkol.)

    1 A   S. „C: Solo"

    19/20 A   B.c.[+ Vla.] Bogensetzung nicht eindeutig

3. *O quam tristis et afflicta*

    A   Bl. 5^v (1. Akkol.) – 6^v

    4–8 B$_{4,5}$ Vla.

    8 A   Vl.I 5. N. mit ♮

    11 A   Vl.II 2. N. mit ♮

    11–13 B$_{4,5}$ Vla.

12 B$_{4,5}$ B.c. 5. N. g statt G

13 B$_{4,5}$ Vl.I [+ II] 6. N. b' statt b

15-18 B$_{4,5}$ Vla.

4. Quae maerebat et dolebat

    A   Bl. 7^r-9^v (1. Akkol.)

1 A   Taktvorzeichnung: „?"

8 A   Vla. 1. N. mit ♭

56 A   Vl.I 2. N. es"; vgl. dagegen T. 46 bzw. T. 85 u. 95

63 A   B.c. [+ Vla.] 2. N. mit ♭

77/78 A   B.c. [+ Vla.] dolce bereits T. 77, 2. Viertel

5. Quis est homo

    A   Bl. 9^v (2. Akkol.) - 11^v (1. Akkol.)

11 A   Vl.II 2. N. mit ♮

13ff. A   Vl.I, II Artikulation schwankt zwischen ♩♪ ♪♪♪♪

           und ♩♪ ♪♪♪♪ ; sie wurde der ersten Form

           entsprechend vereinheitlicht.

17 A   B.c. [+ Vla.] 1. N. mit ♭

20ff. B$_{1-6}$ Vl.I, II ♪♪♪ ♪♪♪ |

40, 44 B$_{2-6}$ A. 1. N. es'

45 A   Vl.I [+ II] forte bereits auf 1. N.

47 A   Vl.I [+ II] dolce bereits auf 1. N.

6. Vidit suum dulcem natum

    A   Bl. 13^r-14^v

3,4 A   Vl.I [+ II] ♪ ♪♪♪ ♪♪♪♪ ♪♪♪ ♪ |

11, 12 A   Vl.I letzte N. ursprünglich ♩ ; nachträglich und
           schlecht lesbar korrigiert zu ♩ ♩

11-13 B$_{1-3}$ Vl.I letzte N. ♩

12, 13 B$_6$ Vl.I letzte N. ♩

24 A   Vl.I [+ II] 1. N. mit ♭

           Vla. col basso; vgl. dagegen T. 22 und B$_{4,5}$

    B$_{4,5}$ Vla.

26-27 A Vl.II

In T. 26 folgte dem punktierten Viertel e'
ursprünglich ein nachschlagendes Achtel c',
das jedoch durchstrichen und durch eine Vier-
telpause ersetzt worden ist. In T. 27 sollte wohl
ursprünglich mit dem 2. Achtel in eine *unisono*-Stimmführung mit Vl.I übergeleitet
werden.

B_{1-6} Vl.II

29 A Vl.I 2. N. mit ♭

30-32 B_{1-3} Vl.I letzte N. ♩

31, 32 B_6 Vl.I letzte N. ♩

7. Eia, mater, fons amoris

A Bl. 15^r-17^r (1. Akkol.)

1 B_5 „Andante"

6 A Vl.I [+ II] 2. N. mit ♭

8 A B.c. [+ Vla.] 2. N. mit ♮

25 A Vl.I 4. N. mit *staccato*-Zeichen

50-56, A Vl.II, B.c. [+ Vla.] Artikulation schwankt
73-79 zwischen ⅋ *etc.* und

etc.

94 A B.c. [+ Vla.]

8. Fac, ut ardeat cor meum

A Bl. 18^r-21^r

4 A Vla. 2. N. mit ♮

9-14 A B.c.

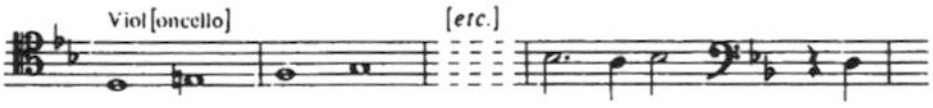

16 A S. 3. N. mit ♭

B.c. 7. N. beziffert mit ♭6

19-21 A B.c.

30 A S. 5.-7. N.

38 A B.c. [+ Vla.] 1. N. mit ♮

40/41 A A.

47 A Vl.I 1. N. mit ♭

68 A   B.c. [+Vla.] 1. N. mit ♭

72 B$_{2,4}$ B.c. [+Vla.] ♩ 𝄐 ‖

9. *Sancta mater istud agas*

A   Bl. 22^r–26^v (1. Akkol.)

1 B$_{4,5}$ „Largo"

6ff. A   Vl. I [+ II] Artikulation schwankt zwischen

♫♫♫♫♫ und ♫♫♫♫♫. ;

sie wurde der ersten Form entsprechend vereinheitlicht.

13 B$_{2,4,5}$ S.  ♫♫. ♪ ♫♫ ♩ |

24 A   Vl. I [+ II] 8. N. mit ♭

37 A   B.c. [+Vla.] 4. N. mit *staccato*-Zeichen

43 A   Vl. II 1. N. mit ♭

49 A   Vl. I 1. N. mit ♭

52 A   Vl. I 9. N. mit ♭

A. 2. N. mit ♭

53 A   Vl. I 4. N. mit ♭

56 A   Vl. I, S. 8. N. mit ♭

57, 61 A   Vl. I 1. N. mit ♭

62, 65 A   B.c. [+Vla.] 1. N. mit ♭

63 A   Vl. II, A. 2. N. mit ♭

10. *Fac, ut portem Christi mortem*

A   Bl. 28^r–29^v (1. Akkol.)

1 B$_4$ „Largo e staccato"

B$_5$ „Mestoso"

12 A   A. 17.–20. N. schlecht lesbar; die Ausgabe folgt
hier der Lesart der Quellen B$_{1-6}$

24 B$_{1-3,6}$ A.  ♪♩ ♫ ♩ |

B$_{4,5}$ A. ab 3. N. freie Auszierung der Kadenz

11. *Inflammatus et accensus*

A   Bl. 29^v (2. Akkol.) – 32^r (1. Akkol.)

2, 4 A   Vla. 3. N. mit ♮

3 A   Vl.I 2.–3. N. mit Bogen

43 A   Vl.II, S. 2. N. mit ♮

48 A   S. 2. N. mit ♮

12. *Quando corpus morietur*

A   Bl. 34r–37r

24 $B_{1-3,6}$ Vl.I [+ II] 9. u. 12. N. mit ♮

A. 3. N. mit ♮

25 $B_{1-3,6}$ A. 1. N. c″

27 $B_{1-3,6}$ Vl. I [+ II] 2. u. 5. N. mit ♮

S. 1. N. mit ♮ ; 2. N. c″ (B_6 : b′)

36–42 A   B.c.

48–52 A   B.c.

73–74 A   S.

78–91 A   Notation in doppelten Takten ($\frac{4}{2}$)

92–94 A   geänderte Lesart durch nachträgliche Einfü-
gung von halben Pausen (S., A., B.c.) und
Korrektur der Viertelnoten zu Halben sowie
der Viertelpausen zu halben Pausen (Vl.I, II):

$B_{4,5}$ folgen der ursprünglichen Lesart in A,
$B_{1-3,6}$ der geänderten (vgl. Vorwort)

STABAT MATER

1. Stabat mater dolorosa

Giovanni Battista Pergolesi
(1710 – 1736)

Edited by Jürgen Neubacher
© 1992 Ernst Eulenburg & Co GmbH
and Ernst Eulenburg Ltd

2

3

EE 6863

4

Siegue C[anto] Solo

2. Cuius animam gementem

Siegue a 2

3. O quam tristis et afflicta

Siegue Alto Solo

4. Quae maerebat et dolebat

5. Quis est homo

6. Vidit suum dulcem natum

A tempo giusto

7. Eia, mater, fons amoris

lu - ge - am, fac,__ ut te - cum lu - ge -

- am, lu - ge - am.

Siegue a 2

8. Fac, ut ardeat cor meum

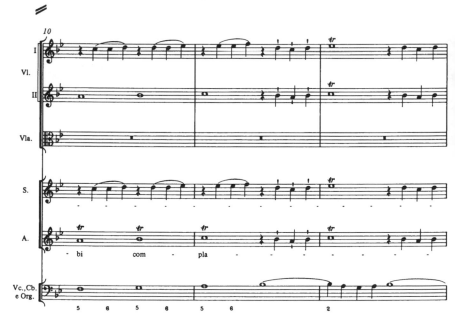

44

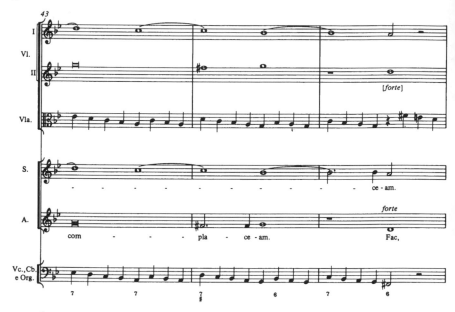

9. Sancta mater, istud agas

10. Fac, ut portem Christi mortem

11. Inflammatus et accensus

In - flam - ma - tus___ et ac - cen - sus

per te,___ vir - go,___ sim de - fen - sus in di - e iu -

- ve - ri, con - fo - ve - ri_ gra - ti - a.
- ve - ri, con - fo - ve - ri_ gra - ti - a.

12. Quando corpus morietur